CHRISTMAS HITS

easy playalong *for* clarinet

WISE PUBLICATIONS
London / New York / Paris / Sydney / Copenhagen / Madrid / Tokyo

Exclusive Distributors:
Music Sales Limited
14-15 Berners Street,
London W1T 3LJ, England.

Music Sales Pty Limited
20 Resolution Drive,
Caringbah, NSW 2229,
Australia.

Order No. AM963138
ISBN 0-7119-8073-X
This book © Copyright 2000 by Wise Publications.

Music compiled and arranged by Paul Honey.
Music processed by Enigma Music Production Services.
Cover photography courtesy George Taylor.
Printed in the United Kingdom by
Caligraving Limited, Thetford, Norfolk.

CD produced by Paul Honey.
Instrumental solos by John Whelan.
All guitars by Arthur Dick.
Engineered by Kester Sims.

Your Guarantee of Quality:
As publishers, we strive to produce every book to
the highest commercial standards.
The music has been freshly engraved and the book
has been carefully designed to minimise awkward page
turns and to make playing from it a real pleasure.
Particular care has been given to specifying acid-free,
neutral-sized paper made from pulps which have not
been elemental chlorine bleached.
This pulp is from farmed sustainable forests and
was produced with special regard for the environment.
Throughout, the printing and binding have been planned
to ensure a sturdy, attractive publication which should
give years of enjoyment.
If your copy fails to meet our high standards,
please inform us and we will gladly replace it.

www.musicsales.com

Clarinet Fingering Chart

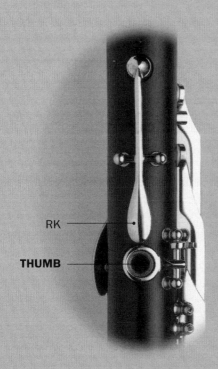

RK

THUMB

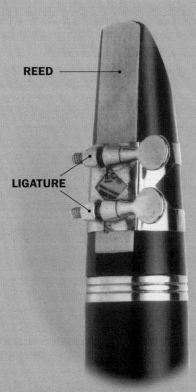

REED

LIGATURE

Mouthpiece

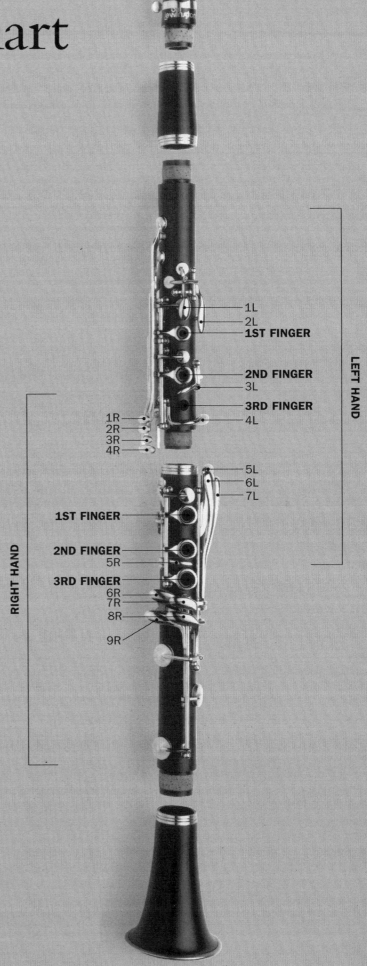

LEFT HAND

1L
2L
1ST FINGER
2ND FINGER
3L
3RD FINGER
4L

1R
2R
3R
4R

5L
6L
7L

RIGHT HAND

1ST FINGER
2ND FINGER
5R
3RD FINGER
6R
7R
8R
9R

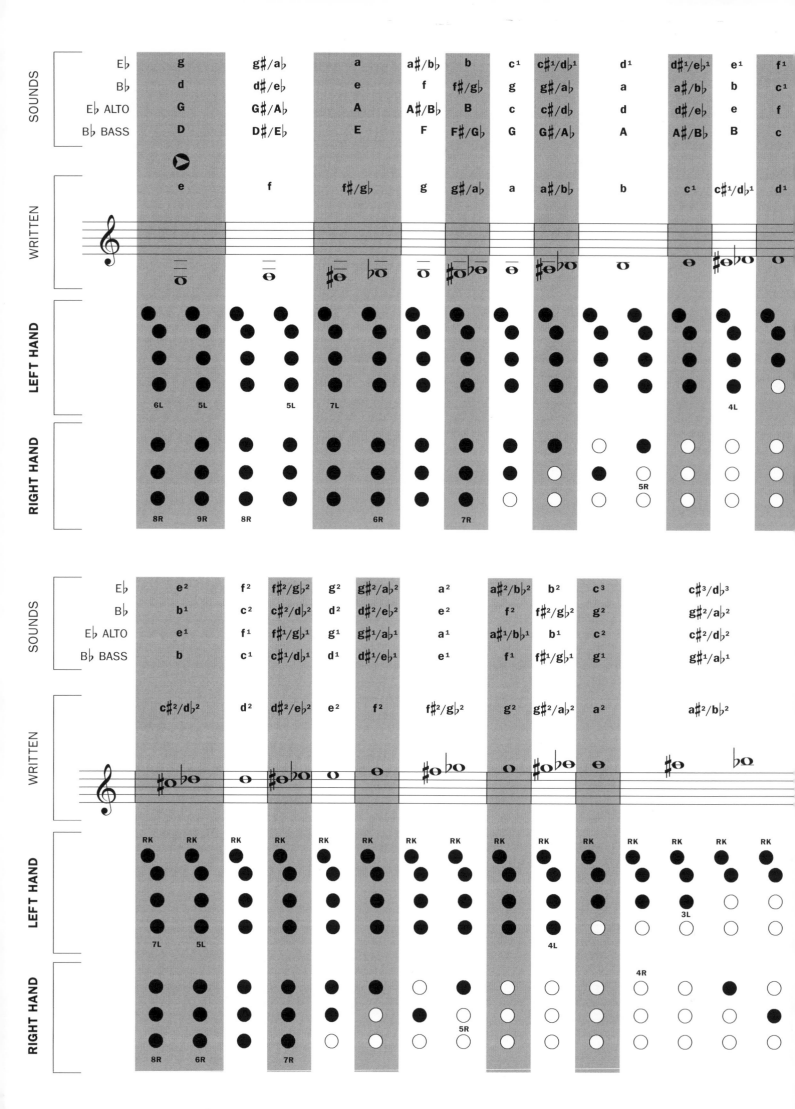

Indicates the lower limit of the best playing range for E♭, B♭, E♭ Alto and B♭ Bass Clarinets

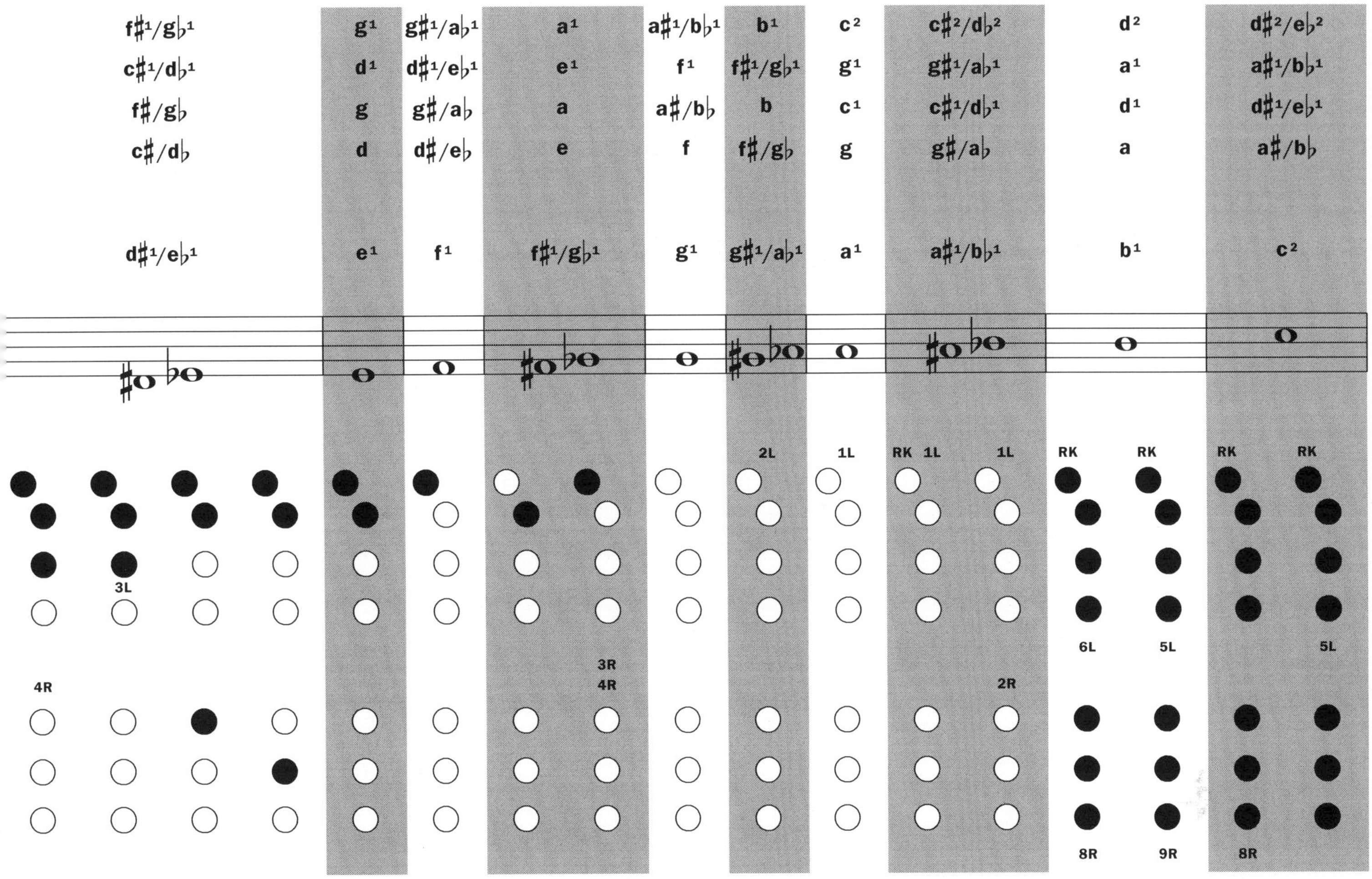
f♯1/g♭1 g1 g♯1/a♭1 a1 a♯1/b♭1 b1 c2 c♯2/d♭2 d2 d♯2/e♭2
c♯1/d♭1 d1 d♯1/e♭1 e1 f1 f♯1/g♭1 g1 g♯1/a♭1 a1 a♯1/b♭1
f♯/g♭ g g♯/a♭ a a♯/b♭ b c1 c♯1/d♭1 d1 d♯1/e♭1
c♯/d♭ d d♯/e♭ e f f♯/g♭ g g♯/a♭ a a♯/b♭
d♯1/e♭1 e1 f1 f♯1/g♭1 g1 g♯1/a♭1 a1 a♯1/b♭1 b1 c2
2L 1L RK 1L 1L RK RK RK RK
3L
6L 5L 5L
4R
3R
4R
2R
8R 9R 8R

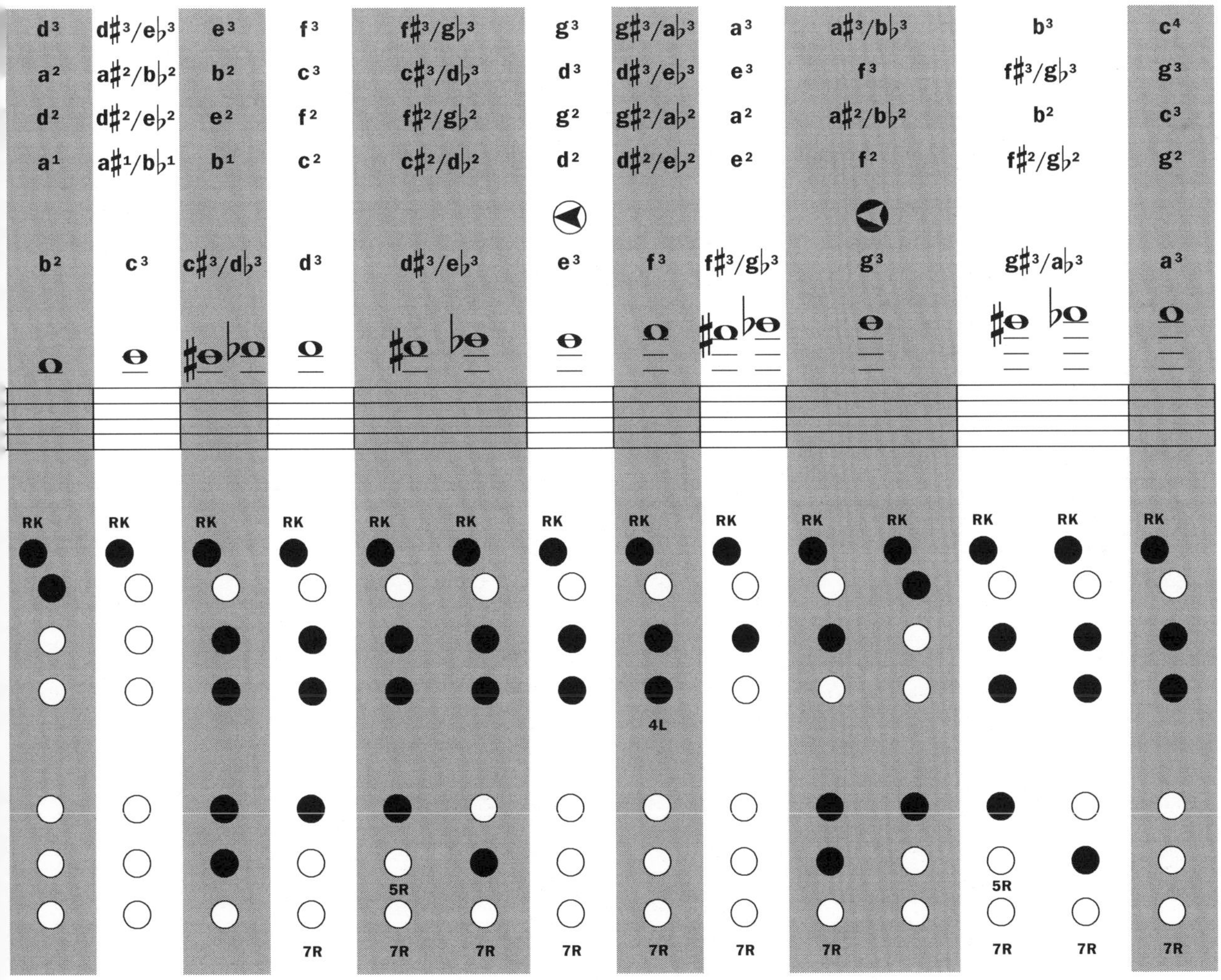
d3 d♯3/e♭3 e3 f3 f♯3/g♭3 g3 g♯3/a♭3 a3 a♯3/b♭3 b3 c4
a2 a♯2/b♭2 b2 c3 c♯3/d♭3 d3 d♯3/e♭3 e3 f3 f♯3/g♭3 g3
d2 d♯2/e♭2 e2 f2 f♯2/g♭2 g2 g♯2/a♭2 a2 a♯2/b♭2 b2 c3
a1 a♯1/b♭1 b1 c2 c♯2/d♭2 d2 d♯2/e♭2 e2 f2 f♯2/g♭2 g2
b2 c3 c♯3/d♭3 d3 d♯3/e♭3 e3 f3 f♯3/g♭3 g3 g♯3/a♭3 a3
RK RK RK RK RK RK RK RK RK RK RK RK RK RK
4L
5R 5R
7R 7R 7R 7R 7R 7R 7R 7R 7R 7R 7R

Indicates the upper limit of the best playing range for E♭ and B♭ Clarinets

Indicates the upper limit of the best playing range for E♭ Alto and B♭ Bass Clarinets

AWAY IN A MANGER

Words: Traditional
Music by William Kirkpatrick

lit - tle Lord Je - sus no___ cry - ing He makes. I

love thee, Lord___ Je - sus, look___ down from the sky, and___

stay by my side un - til___ morn - ing is nigh.

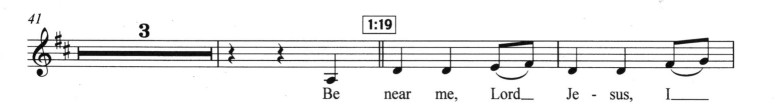

1:19

Be near me, Lord___ Je - sus, I___

ask thee to stay close___ by me for - ev - er and___

love me, I pray. Bless all the dear___ child - ren in___ Thy ten - der

poco rall.

care, and___ fit us for hea - ven to___ live with Thee there.

FROSTY THE SNOWMAN

Words & Music by Steve Nelson & Jack Rollins

Moderately

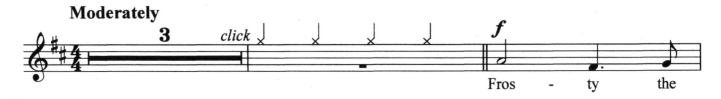

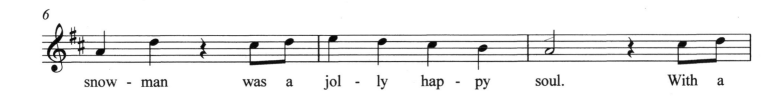

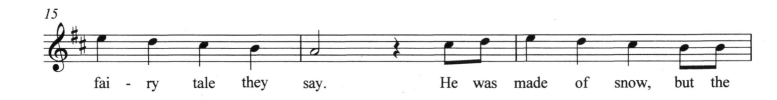

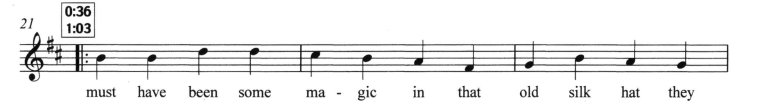

must have been some ma-gic in that old silk hat they

found, for when they placed it on his head, he be-

-gan to dance a - round. Oh, Fros - ty the

snow - man was a - live as he could be, and the

child - ren say he could laugh and play just the same as you and

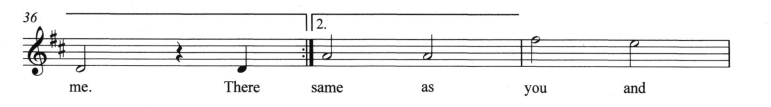

me. There same as you and

me._____

GOOD KING WENCESLAS

Traditional

Good King Wen - ces - las looked out

on the Feast of Ste - phen. When the snow lay round a - bout,

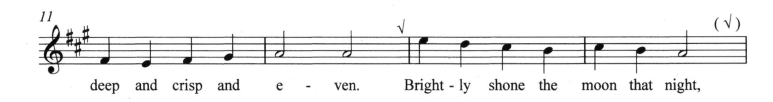

deep and crisp and e - ven. Bright - ly shone the moon that night,

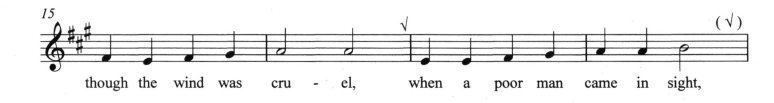

though the wind was cru - el, when a poor man came in sight,

gath - 'ring win - ter fu - el. "Hi- ther, page and

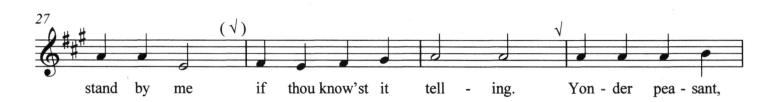

stand by me if thou know'st it tell - ing. Yon - der pea - sant,

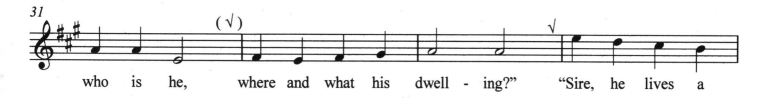

who is he, where and what his dwell - ing?" "Sire, he lives a

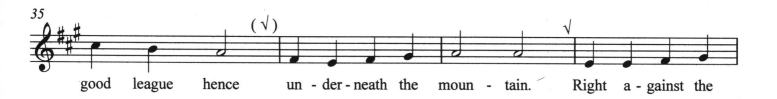

good league hence un - der - neath the moun - tain. Right a - gainst the

fo - rest fence by St. Ag - nes foun - - tain."

Page and mo - narch

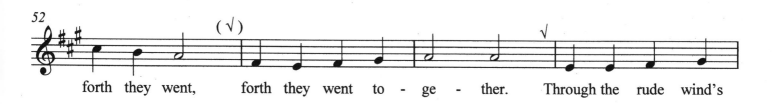

forth they went, forth they went to - ge - ther. Through the rude wind's

wild lam - ent and the bit - ter wea - - - ther.

HAPPY XMAS (WAR IS OVER)

Words & Music by John Lennon & Yoko Ono

I BELIEVE IN FATHER CHRISTMAS

Words & Music by Greg Lake & Peter Sinfield

They said there'll be snow at Christ-mas, they said there'll be peace on Earth. But in-stead it just kept on rain-ing, a veil of tears for the vir-gin birth. I re-mem-ber one Christ-mas morn-ing, a win-ter's light and a dis-tant choir and the peal of a bell and that Christ-mas tree smell and eyes full of tin-sel and fire.

I WISH IT COULD BE CHRISTMAS EVERY DAY

Words & Music by Roy Wood

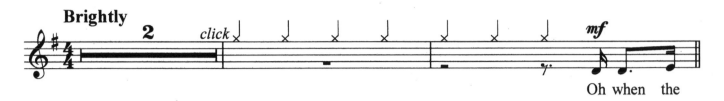

Oh when the

snow - man brings the snow, oh well he just might like to

know he's put a great big smile on some - bo - dy's

face.___ If you jump in - to your

bed, quick - ly cov - er up your head, don't you

lock the doors, you know that sweet San - ta Claus is on the way.___

Oh well I wish it could be Christ - mas ev - 'ry

day._____ When the kids start sing - ing and the

band be - gins to play._____ Oh I wish it could be

Christ - mas ev - 'ry day._____ So let the bells ring

out for Christ - mas. Oh well I Christ - mas._____

_____ Why don't you give your love for Christ - mas?

JINGLE BELLS

Words & Music by J.S. Pierpont

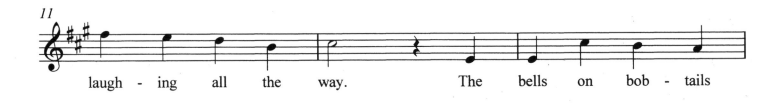

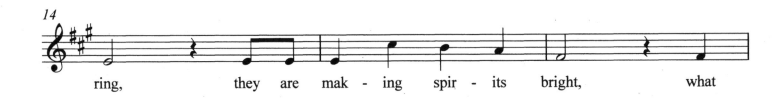

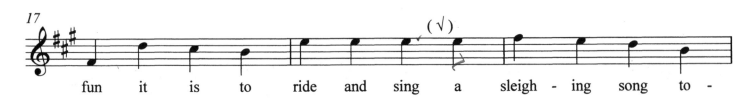

LAST CHRISTMAS

Words & Music by George Michael

ve - ry next day you gave it a - way.__ This year__ to

save me from tears I'll give it to some-one spe - cial.

Last Christ - mas I gave you my heart, but the ve - ry next day you

gave it a - way.__ This year__ to save me from tears I'll

give it to some - one spe - cial.

MERRY XMAS EVERYBODY

Words & Music by Neville Holder & James Lea

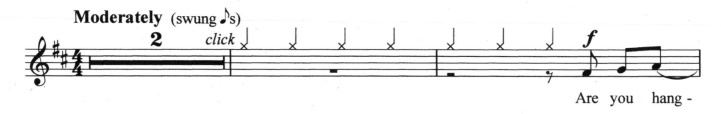

Are you hang-

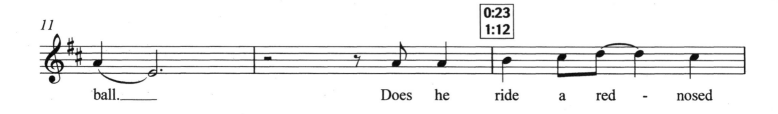

-ing up a stock - ing on your wall?___

It's the time___ that ev - 'ry San - ta has___ a

ball.___ Does he ride a red - nosed

rein - deer? Does a 'ton up' on___ his sleigh,___ do the

fair - ies keep___ him so - ber for___ a day?___

So here it is, Mer - ry Christ - mas, ev - 'ry -

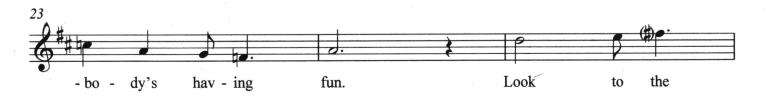

- bo - dy's hav - ing fun. Look to the

fu - ture now, it's on - ly just be - gun.

_____ Are you hang - So here it

is, Mer - ry Christ mas, ev - 'ry - bo - dy's hav - ing

fun. Look to the fu - ture now, it's

on - ly just be - gun.

MISTLETOE AND WINE

Words by Leslie Stewart & Jeremy Paul
Music by Keith Strachan

O LITTLE TOWN OF BETHLEHEM

Words by Phillips Brooks
Music by Lewis Redner

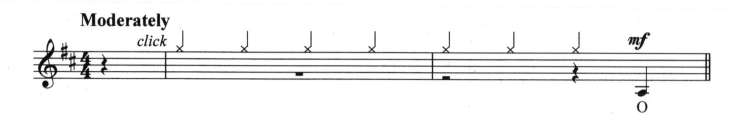

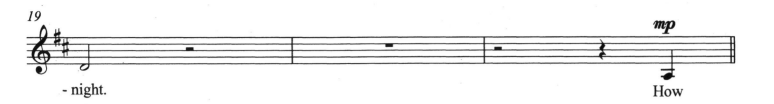

- night. How

si - lent - ly, how si - lent - ly the wond - rous__ gift is

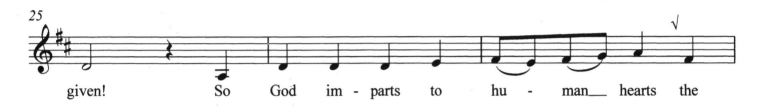

given! So God im - parts to hu - man__ hearts the

bless - ing__ of his heaven. No__ ear may hear__ His__

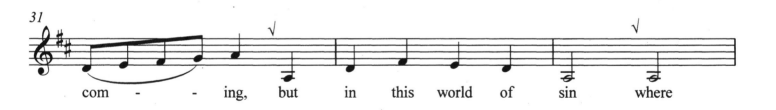

com - - ing, but in this world of sin where

meek souls will re - ceive__ Him__ still the dear Christ__ en - ters

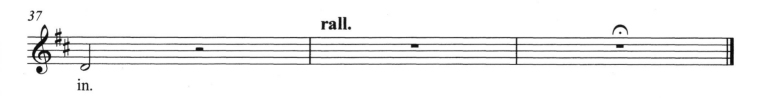

rall.

in.

SILENT NIGHT

Words by Joseph Mohr
Music by Franz Gruber

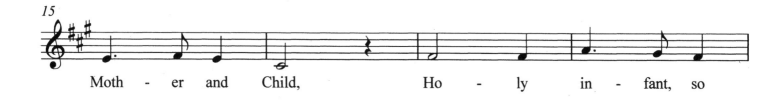

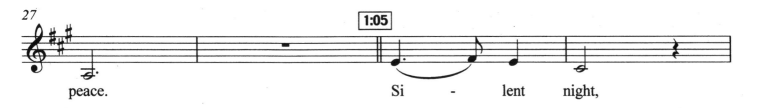

27 peace. **1:05** Si - lent night,

31 ho - ly night! Shep - herds quake

35 at the sight. **1:23** Glo - ries stream_____ from

39 Heav - en a - far, Heav - n'ly hosts_____ sing

43 Al - le - lu - ia. **1:42** Christ the Sav - iour is

47 born!_____ Christ__ the Sav - iour is born.

STOP THE CAVALRY

Words & Music by Jona Lewie

Hey, Mis-ter Chur-chill comes ov-er here to say we're_ do-ing splen-did-ly. But it's ve-ry cold out here in the snow, march-ing to and from the e-ne-my. Oh, I say it's tough, I have had e-nough, can you stop the ca-val-ry? I have had to fight al-most ev-'ry night down through-out_ the cen-tu-ries. That is when I say, oh yes yet a-gain, can you stop the ca-val-ry? Ma-ry proud-ly waits at home in the nuc-le-ar fall-out zone. Wish I could_ be danc-ing now

32

in the arms_ of the girl I love.___   Du bu du bu dum dum

38

du bu du bu dum, du bu dum dum du bu dum du bu du bu dum.

41

Du bu du bu dum dum du bu du bu dum, du bu dum dum du bu dum

44

du bu du bu dum. Wish I was a home___ for Christ-mas.___

49   1:20

Wish I could_ be danc-ing now in the arms_ of the girl I know.

53

Ma-ry proud-ly waits at home, she's been wait-ing two years long.___

58

Wish I was at home___ for Christ-mas.___

WINTER WONDERLAND

Words by Richard Smith
Music by Felix Bernard

Lazy swing (swung ♪s)

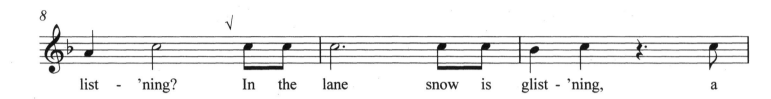

Sleigh bells ring, are you

list - 'ning? In the lane snow is glist - 'ning, a

beau - ti - ful sight,__ we're hap - py to - night,__ walk - in' in a win - ter won - der-

- land. Gone a - way is the blue - bird, here to stay is a

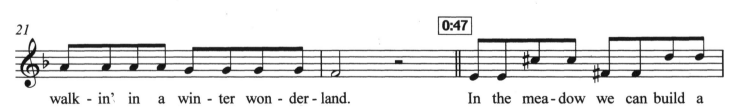

new bird, he sings a love song,__ as we go a - long,__

walk - in' in a win - ter won - der - land. In the mea - dow we can build a

snow - man, then pre - tend that he is Par - son Brown.

He'll say "Are you mar - ried?" We'll say "No, Man, but you can do the job when you're in

town." La - ter on we'll con - spire___ as we dream by the

fire___ to face un - a - fraid,_ the plans that we made,_

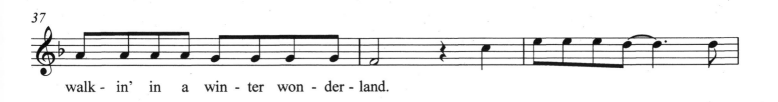

walk - in' in a win - ter won - der - land.

HARK! THE HERALD ANGELS SING

Music by Felix Mendelssohn
Words by Charles Wesley

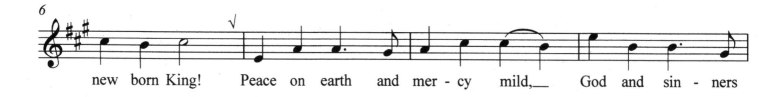

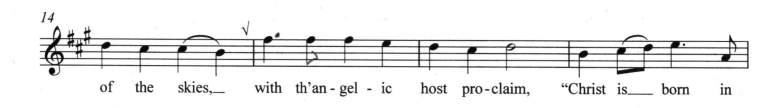

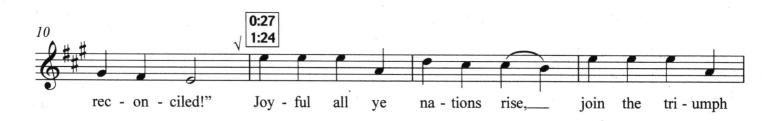

8/12 (184116)